STEM *Activit*

SENSATIONAL
SCIENCE

Published in 2018 by Carlton Books Limited
An imprint of the Carlton Publishing Group
20 Mortimer Street, London W1T 3JW

A catalogue record for this book is available from the
British Library.

ISBN: 978-1-78312-359-9

Printed in China
10 9 8 7 6 5 4 3 2 1

Executive editor: Bryony Davies
Editor: Selina Wood
Design: Kate Wiliwinska
Designed and packaged by: The Shop
Illustrated by: Dynamo Limited
Picture research: Steve Behan and Paul Langan
Production: Nicola Davey

AUTHOR:

STEPHANIE CLARKSON is a writer and
journalist, and has been writing for children for the past
decade. Her experience allows her to excel at making
complex subject areas accessible to young readers and
she has penned educational and non-fiction titles for
leading trade publishers on current affairs, technology,
art, travel and mental health.

STEM EDITORIAL CONSULTANT:
MARGARET (MEG) KÄUFER is a
founding member and current President of the STEM
Alliance of Larchmont-Mamaroneck, NY. The STEM
Alliance is a non-profit organisation with the mission of
creating a network of STEM learning opportunities to
connect today's youth to the jobs of the future. They work
closely with local schools to run hands-on, applied STEM
enrichment experiences. Highlights of their work under
her leadership include launching an annual public STEM
festival, establishing competitive robotics teams, and
creating a hands-on STEM summer enrichment program
for at-risk children. Meg has her Masters in Curriculum
& Instruction from Teachers College — Columbia
University. Throughout her career, Meg has championed
STEM learning for its capacity to engage and inspire all
varieties of learners.

PICTURE ACKNOWLEDGEMENTS
The publishers would like to thank the following sources for their kind
permission to reproduce the pictures in the book.

Pages 6-7: Alexandr III/Shutterstock; 9 (top right): Public Domain; 12
(bottom left) Juan Gaertner/Shutterstock; 17 (top right) NASA; 18
(bottom left) Manzrussali/Shutterstock; 20 (left) Library of Congress;
22 (top right) Public Domain, (bottom right) Chinasong/Shutterstock;
23 (bottom right) Boonchuay Promjiam/Shutterstock; 24 (top) Serega
K Photo and Video/Shutterstock; 25 (bottom) VanderWolf Images/
Shutterstock; 26 (top right) Library of Congress; 27 (bottom) Photobank
Gallery/Shutterstock; 29 (top right) Ivan Lukyanchuk/Shutterstock;
30 (left) Georgios Kollidas/Shutterstock; 31 (top right) Macrovector/
Shutterstock; 32 (left) Titov Nikolai/Shutterstock; 34 (top left) Photobort/
Shutterstock, (top right) David Ryo/Shutterstock, (left) Antonio Truzzi/
Shutterstock, (right) Lars Hallstrom/Shutterstock, (bottom left)
MLArduengo/Shutterstock, (bottom right) Paul Wishart/Shutterstock;
35 (top) CERN Photo Lab; 38 (key) Aboikis/Shutterstock, (log)
FotografFF/Shutterstock, (cat) Hannadarzy/Shutterstock, (egg) Vankad/
Shutterstock; 40 (top) SlayStorm/Shutterstock; 41 (top) Sumire8/
Shutterstock; 43 (top) Bess Hamitii/Shutterstock; 44 (top) Guten Tag
Vector/Shutterstock; 45 (humpback whale) Tomas Kotouc/Shutterstock,
(shark) Zebra0209/Shutterstock, (spider web) SJ Travel Photo and
Video/Shutterstock, (butterfly wings) Jps/Shutterstock, (burrs) Jackan/
Shutterstock, (kingfisher) Rudmer Zwerver/Shutterstock, (tablet)
Lucadp/Shutterstock, (velcro) Daniel Brasil/Shutterstock, (wind turbine)
Diyanski/Shutterstock, (train) Wayne0216/Shutterstock, (swimming
costume) XiXinXing/Shutterstock, (tape) Kwangmoozaa/Shutterstock;
46 (bottom right) La Gorda/Shutterstock; 47 (top right) Chokniti
Khongchum/Shutterstock; 49 (centre) Studio concept/Shutterstock,
(bottom left) Mark Nazh/Shutterstock; 50 (left) Universal History
Archive/UIG/Getty Images; 51 (top right) Rudmer Zwerver/Shutterstock;
52 (bottom left) Monet_3k/Shutterstock, (bottom centre) Public Domain,
(bottom right) Dave Guttridge/Imperial College London; 57 (centre)
Natural History Museum of Utah; 59 (top right) Sakdinon Kadchiangsaen/
Shutterstock; 60 (top right) Shawn Hempel/Shutterstock, (bottom)
AllNikart/Shutterstock

Every effort has been made to acknowledge correctly and
contact the source and/or copyright holder of each picture,
and Carlton Books apologises for any unintentional
errors or omissions, which will be corrected in
future editions of this book.

SCIENCE TECHNOLOGY ENGINEERING MATHS

STEM Activity

SENSATIONAL
SCIENCE

Stephanie Clarkson

CARLTON KIDS

CONTENTS

SUPER STEM

Welcome to the world of STEM. STEM stands for science, technology, engineering and maths. These four fabulous subjects open up a world of exciting discovery.

You probably already possess many of the qualities and interests shared by great scientists, technologists, engineers and mathematicians. Read each statement and put a tick in the box if it applies to you.

SCIENCE

YOU...

- are curious about the world around you. ☐

- love to ask questions. ☐

- experiment and try new things, even if it means making a mistake. ☐

You're already on your way to becoming a scientist! This book will help you to discover more about the way scientists think and work.

TECHNOLOGY

YOU...

- are always playing with gadgets. ☐

- like to understand exactly how machines work. ☐

- try to find ways of making everyday tasks easier, such as investigating whether a different route to school makes the journey shorter. ☐

Technology is right up your street! You're fascinated by the latest products and want to find out more about inventions that help to improve our world.

ENGINEERING

YOU...

- like using your brain to solve problems. ☐

- love playing with construction sets and building bricks. ☐

- enjoy building amazing dens or dams in streams. ☐

You're perfectly suited to a career as an engineer! You could invent or make amazing tools, machines and buildings.

MATHS

YOU...

- like to understand the reasons why something is true. ☐

- often spot patterns such as in pictures or clothing and sequences in numbers like football statistics. ☐

- love 3D puzzles, card games and logic games like chess and battleships. ☐

You're a born mathematician! You're excited by shapes and measurements, and curious to see just what numbers can do when you use them in different ways.

WHAT IS SCIENCE?

This book is all about science. Science is our way of finding answers to the mysteries of life. Scientists want to help improve our understanding of the history of the world, and how our Universe works. Scientists ask questions about the world around them, make predictions, then test those theories and organise and share their knowledge.

There are still many mysteries scientists are working to solve. Perhaps one day you will help find out how our brains work or answer age-old questions such as why gravity only pulls? You might even use hands-on science to solve problems such as how to make biodegradable plastic, or to prove whether there is alien life in our Universe. Science is all around us!

FIELDS OF SCIENCE

Scientists can study anything from the tiniest microorganism to vast areas of outer space. There are many different areas of science. Each can help us to answer questions and improve our understanding of the world around us.

ACTIVITY

Can you draw an arrow to match each branch of science up to the right explanation? The first one has been done for you.

1 BIOTECHNOLOGY

2 BIOLOGY

3 CHEMISTRY

4 EARTH SCIENCE

5 PHYSICS

6 SPACE SCIENCE

7 BIOCHEMISTRY

8 BIOMEDICINE

A   The study of living things to find medical treatments.

B   The study of our planet.

C   The study of the chemical processes of living things.

D   The study of living things.

E   The study of the Universe.

F   The study of substances that make up matter.

G   The study and use of parts of living things to make other products.

H   The study of energy and forces.

CHECK THE ANSWERS AT THE BACK OF THE BOOK!

THE HISTORY OF SCIENCE

In ancient times, people made up stories to explain things they couldn't understand. Things started to change about 2,500 years ago when Greek thinkers began to question the workings of the Universe by looking at the natural world around them.

ACTIVITY

Archimedes' principle, the law of buoyancy, is still used today. It describes how ships float. Crack the code to discover what Archimedes said when he made his big discovery.

CODE KEY

A	B	C	D	E	F	G
?	$	9	\	7	~	4

H	I	J	K	L	M	N
6	&	^	+	8	=	(

O	P	Q	R	S	T	U
3	/	1	%	*	}	@

V	W	X	Y	Z
)	!	5	-	2

7	@	%	7	+	?
E	V	R	E	K	A

ARCHIMEDES

Archimedes lived in Sicily, Italy between 287-212 BCE. One day he noticed that some water spilled over the edge of his bathtub as he got in. As a result, he came up with a brand new principle to explain whether an object floats or sinks.

THINK LIKE A SCIENTIST

Modern scientists use a special method to help them work. First they ask a question. Next, they conduct research, gathering information around the subject, and form a hypothesis (a prediction). They then test with experiments and record their results.

THE SCIENTIFIC METHOD

The scientific method will help you to think like a scientist.

QUESTION
I wonder what happens if...

HYPOTHESIS (PREDICTION) BASED ON RESEARCH
I think...

EXPERIMENT
I see...

RESULTS
I found...

CONCLUSION
I think this means...

SHARE
I learned that...

Scientists come up with lots of interesting theories about the world and how it works, but a theory can't be accepted until it has been properly tested. Scientists use results to repeat and test past experiments, and to create their own new ones.

ACTIVITY

These scientists are in a laboratory working on an experiment.
Look carefully at the pictures. Can you spot the odd one out?

 A

 B

C

D

OUR UNIVERSE

Our Universe is everything we can touch, feel, sense, measure and detect. It is made up of billions of galaxies and it contains billions of stars. No one knows what shape the Universe is, nor its exact size, but we know it is vast because even using special instruments, we can't see the edge.

Objects that are bigger than a planet, but smaller than a star are known as Brown Dwarfs. These are much cooler than stars, so they don't burn bright enough to be seen with the naked eye.

THE BIG BANG

The Big Bang theory states that about 13.7 billion years ago all the matter in the Universe was concentrated into a single tiny point that rapidly expanded in a huge explosion.

Asteroids are rocky, airless worlds that orbit our Sun. They are too small to be called planets. Scientists keep a close watch on asteroids that may pass close to Earth. These are called NEOs (Near-Earth Objects).

ACTIVITY

Can you place these objects found in space in order from the biggest to the smallest?

BROWN DWARF
ASTEROID
STAR
GALAXY
PLANET
UNIVERSE

BIG

univures

Galaxy

Star

Brown dwarf

Planet

Asteroid

SMALL

CHECK THE ANSWERS AT THE BACK OF THE BOOK!

SPLENDID SPACE

Outer space begins around 100 km above the Earth. It is a vacuum with no air, which means that sound cannot travel through it. If you were floating in space, no one could hear you talk, shout or even scream!

IS SPACE BLACK?

Space only **appears** dark. Earth's atmosphere is full of particles that scatter light from the Sun, creating a blue sky. But in space, the atmosphere does not contain enough particles and objects to scatter light.

ACTIVITY

The International Space Station (ISS) is an astronaut's home away from home. Draw arrows to insert the missing pieces from this picture of the ISS.

The ISS is the biggest object ever flown in space. It orbits the Earth 16 times a day.

A

B

C

D

CHECK THE ANSWERS AT THE BACK OF THE BOOK!

THE SOLAR SYSTEM

For thousands of years, people thought the Sun and planets moved around the Earth. Then astronomers proved the Sun was actually at the centre. The solar system is made up of the Sun, the eight planets and everything else that revolves around it.

SUN

MERCURY
The planet closest to the Sun.

VENUS
The hottest planet in our solar system.

EARTH
The only planet in our solar system to support life.

MARS
Known as the 'Red Planet' because of its red soil, which contains iron oxide (rust).

ACTIVITY

A mnemonic device is a saying that can help you remember the order of the planets. Each word in the saying begins with the same letter as the planet that you are trying to remember in order. **'My Very Excited Mother Just Served Us Nachos'** is an example of a mnemonic device.
Can you make up one of your own?

M ~~ercur~~ y

V ery

E vil

M ouse

J ust

S hook

U nder grand

N ails

JUPITER

The largest planet, it has no solid surface.

SATURN

Circled by rings made of ice and rock.

URANUS

The only planet with a horizontal axis instead of a vertical axis, so it spins on its side.

NEPTUNE

A cold planet with 13 moons.

The Sun won't last forever. Scientists have learned that it will continue to burn its hydrogen and helium fuel for another billion years, expanding to around a hundred times its current size and swallowing up all the planets in the solar system, including Earth.

EX-PLANET PLUTO

Until 2006 Pluto was known as the ninth planet from the Sun, but it was demoted when the definition of a planet was changed. It is now known as a 'dwarf planet'.

ACTIVITY

We rely on the Sun to survive. Without its light and heat, our planet would freeze and life on Earth would end. The Sun is an enormous, 4.5 billion-year-old star that holds our solar system together.

Bring this flower to life by colouring it in.

MAGNIFICENT MOON

The Moon is the brightest object in the sky, but it has no light of its own. It appears to shine because it reflects the light from the Sun. The part of the Moon facing away from the Sun is in darkness.

The Moon takes just over 27 days to orbit the Earth. It is around 384,400 km away from our planet. If you were to travel there by car it would take around 130 days, driving at 129 km/h.

ACTIVITY

As the Moon travels around the Earth, it looks as if it's changing shape in the sky. This is because we are seeing the Moon lit up by the Sun in different ways on different days.

Can you complete the rest of the lunar cycle? Colour in the pale purple moons to show the portions that are in shade.

Waxing gibbous

First quarter

Waxing crescent

Sun

Full Moon

New Moon

Waning gibbous

Waning crescent

Last quarter

The Moon rises and sets each day like the Sun, but unlike the Sun, the moonrise and moonset times change as it moves through its cycle.

CHECK THE ANSWERS AT THE BACK OF THE BOOK!

THE STARS

There are at least a billion trillion stars in the Universe. There are more stars than grains of sand on all of the beaches on Earth. Each star is a burning ball of gas that exists for billions of years.

NANCY GRACE ROMAN

Born in America in 1925, Nancy Roman organised a backyard astronomy club for her friends when she was just 11. She went on to become NASA's first chief of astronomy, helping develop amazing orbiting telescopes.

ACTIVITY

Connect the stars to create Canis Major — the Great Dog Constellation.

DID YOU KNOW?

Groups of stars that form a recognizable shape or pattern are known as **constellations**.

Sirius

LET THERE BE LIGHT

Light travels as waves and in straight lines. Objects don't give off their own light. It is the light bouncing off an object that allows us to see it.

When a ray of sunlight comes to Earth the light seems white. In fact it's made up of a spectrum of colours. A triangular block of glass called a prism can be used to split light into separate colours that we can see.

ACTIVITY

In nature, raindrops can refract white light into colours. Unscramble the letters to discover what we see when this happens.

B A N O W I R

....

Within this visible spectrum, the wavelength of light determines the colour. For example, blue and green have shorter wavelengths than yellow, orange and red light.

Light travels much faster than sound, which is why we see lightning or a firework explode before we hear them.

A reflection is created when light is bounced off a surface. If the surface is smooth like metal on the back of a mirror or a smooth pond, the reflection is sharp.

ACTIVITY

Use a pen to complete the boy's reflection in the mirror.

Optical sensors in fire alarms can detect the UV rays in flames. They are often used for fire alarms in restaurants or homes.

ELECTRICITY

Electricity didn't have to be invented as it exists naturally in our world — it can be seen during thunderstorms when lightning bolts shoot down from the sky. Electricity that builds up in one place is called static electricity. Electricity that travels from one place to another is called current electricity.

Electricity is the flow of tiny particles called electrons. Each electron carries a tiny amount of electric charge. A bolt of lightning is caused by a build up of electrons created by friction from ice crystals in a storm cloud.

THOMAS EDISON

Thomas Edison is often described as America's greatest inventor. In 1879, he invented the electric light bulb. The first bulb was an airtight glass container with a wire inside it.

In 1752, Benjamin Franklin wanted to prove that lightning was a form of electricity. He flew a kite during a thunderstorm and tied a metal key to a wet kite string to conduct the electricity. Electricity from the storm clouds flowed down the wet string and gave him a shock.

!

Franklin could have been badly hurt or killed if his kite had been struck by lightning. This is not something you should **ever** try.

ACTIVITY

Complete each circuit by adding and naming the missing part.

An electrical circuit is a complete, unbroken path through which electricity can flow. Each circuit needs a switch, a power source (such as a battery), a load (such as a light bulb) and an uninterrupted pathway of wires between them.

Power source

Switch

Pathway

Light bulb

What's broken?

A

What's missing?

B

What's missing?

C

What's missing?

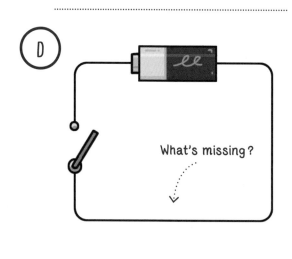

D

CHECK THE ANSWERS AT THE BACK OF THE BOOK!

AMAZING X-RAYS

X-rays are a type of electromagnetic radiation. An X-ray's wavelength is smaller than that of an ultraviolet ray, which means that the human eye can't see it.

ACTIVITY

Colour the shapes with an x in them black, to create an X-ray picture.

WILHELM RÖNTGEN

In 1895, Wilhelm Röntgen made a discovery that changed medical science. He found that some invisible rays could pass through the soft parts of a body to create a photographic image. He called these strange new rays X-rays!

Doctors use X-ray pictures to check for broken bones. Airports use them to look for unsafe objects inside bags and suitcases.

CHECK THE ANSWERS AT THE BACK OF THE BOOK!

SOUND

Sound travels in waves. These invisible vibrations move through air, water and solid objects and are then picked up by our ears. The size and shape of a sound wave changes the type of sound that we can hear.

DID YOU KNOW?

Each sound has a wavelength. The frequency of the sound waves and the energy in the sound waves determines volume and pitch.

Soft (less energy)

Loud (more energy)

Low pitch (long wavelength)

High pitch (short wavelength)

ACTIVITY

Circle the sounds with short wavelengths.

MOUSE

DOLPHIN

OPERA SINGER

LION

DRUM

WHISTLE

TRACTOR

ALARM CLOCK

6:30

THUNDERSTORM

SEEING WITH SOUND

Bats and whales use sound to find their way around. Through a process called echolocation, they send out sounds that echo off the objects around them, letting them know where the object is.

23

ENERGY

In science, energy is described as the ability to do work. Everything needs energy to change and move, including living things. Energy is never created or destroyed, it is only changed from one state to another.

RENEWABLE VS NON-RENEWABLE

We get most of our energy from non-renewable energy sources like fossil fuels, natural gas, coal and uranium (a substance used to make electricity). Our planet only has a certain amount of these sources. Once they are used, they are gone.

Today, scientists are looking to harness new renewable energy from natural resources that can be replenished and replaced, such as wind and fast-growing plants.

There are lots of different types of energy and they all come from somewhere or something. The chemical energy that you use to move your body comes from the food you eat and the air you breathe. Outdoor heat energy comes from the Sun.

Another problem with non-renewable fossil fuels is that burning them pollutes our air with dangerous gases like carbon dioxide.

ACTIVITY

Read the clues. Now unscramble the letters to find the renewable energy sources.
The words you need are shown underneath the puzzle.

1 Power from a burning star around which we orbit.

R O S A L

_ _ _ _ _

2 Turbines on hills are used to capture this power.

N D I W

_ _ _ _

3 This source is plant-based.

O D O W

_ _ _ _

4 This power is sourced from the movement of the oceans and seas.

L I T A D

_ _ _ _ _

| WOOD | WIND | SOLAR | TIDAL |

Electric cars do not use petrol or non-renewable energy. Tesla, an all-electric car, is named after the Serbian-American electrical engineer and physicist Nikola Tesla. Tesla invented the first alternating current motor.

CHECK THE ANSWERS AT THE BACK OF THE BOOK!

HEAT

Heat energy is measured in joules. It is the result of the movements of tiny particles. These are always in motion, vibrating or bumping into each other. The motion of the particles creates a form of energy called heat that is present in all matter.

ACTIVITY

Circle the objects that are conductors.

Conductors are materials that let heat pass easily through them. Insulators are materials that don't allow heat to pass easily through them.

ALBERT EINSTEIN

Albert Einstein was one of the greatest scientists that ever lived. His groundbreaking theory of relativity $E = MC^2$ proved that mass is another form of energy, just like heat or light.

FRYING PAN

RUBBER HOT WATER BOTTLE

WOODEN DOOR

WOOLLEN GLOVES

RADIATOR

METAL SPOON

PLASTIC WATER BOTTLE

IRON

RING

TEMPERATURE

Temperature is not the same as heat. While heat is the total amount of energy of all the molecules stored inside something, temperature is a measurement of how hot or cold it is.

ACTIVITY

Temperature is measured in degrees Celsius (°C) or Fahrenheit (°F).
Colour in the mercury in the thermometers to show each animal's body temperature.

HUMAN
98.6°F/37°C

°F °C
120 — — 50
— — 40
100 —
— — 30
80 —
— — 20
60 —
— — 10
40 —
— — 0

CHICKEN
107.6°F/42°C

°F °C
120 — — 50
— — 40
100 —
— — 30
80 —
— — 20
60 —
— — 10
40 —
— — 0

COW
102°F/39°C

°F °C
120 — — 50
— — 40
100 —
— — 30
80 —
— — 20
60 —
— — 10
40 —
— — 0

Earth's average surface temperature has risen 1.1 °C since the late 19th century. This global warming is contributing to shrinking polar ice caps and warming oceans, putting many species of animal at risk and leading to extreme weather events.

CHECK THE ANSWERS AT THE BACK OF THE BOOK!

FABULOUS FORCES

You can't see them, but forces make our world go round. A force is really just a push or a pull. Adding force to an object by pushing or pulling results in motion. The physicist Isaac Newton described three Laws of Motion that explain how forces work on objects.

ACTIVITY

It takes force for this boy to push his shopping cart to the checkout. If he stops pushing, the cart will stop moving. Trace his path through the mini-maze.

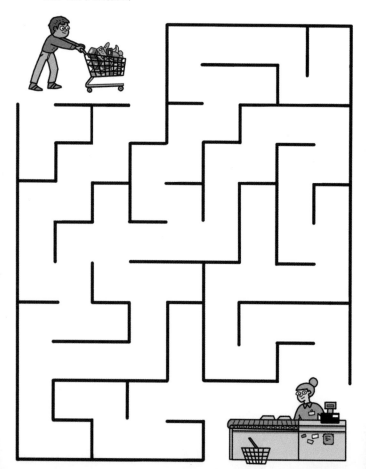

FIRST LAW

An object at rest will stay at rest and an object in motion will stay in motion with the same direction or speed unless acted upon by an external force.

When you are in a car travelling at speed, if the car brakes you will continue going forward (until the car comes to rest or you are stopped by the force of the seatbelt).

SECOND LAW

The acceleration of an object is directly related to the strength of the force applied to it.

When we kick a ball we exert force in a specific direction. The harder we kick the ball, the stronger the force applied to it and the further it will travel.

THIRD LAW

For every action or force, there is an equal and opposite reaction or force.

When you sit on a chair, the chair needs to exert an equal force upwards or the chair will collapse.

CHECK THE ANSWERS AT THE BACK OF THE BOOK!

Friction is a 'grip-like' force that holds back the motion of a moving object. It happens wherever objects come into contact with each other. Friction in gases, such as pushing a paper aeroplane through air, is called air resistance or drag.

ACTIVITY

Look at each picture. Decide whether it shows useful friction, too much friction or not enough friction.

If you are running on the pavement and want to stop, the friction between the soles of your shoes and the cement will help you stop more quickly. If you were running on a patch of ice it would take longer, because the surface is smooth and there is less friction between the ice and your shoe.

1 Someone with a ring stuck on their finger.

2 Someone striking a match.

3 Someone rubbing their hands together to keep warm.

4 Someone sledging.

5 Car tyres on a road.

6 Someone slipping over on ice.

USEFUL FRICTION   TOO MUCH FRICTION   NOT ENOUGH FRICTION

CHECK THE ANSWERS AT THE BACK OF THE BOOK!

GRAVITY

Gravity is a force by which a planet draws objects towards its centre. Gravity holds our world and solar system together, keeping planets in orbit around the Sun and the Moon in orbit around the Earth.

DID YOU KNOW?

Anything that has mass also has gravity. Objects with more mass have more gravity. This is why Jupiter, a larger planet, has a stronger gravitational pull than Earth, while Mercury, a smaller planet, has less.

Gravity is invisible, so how do we know it's there? If you jump in the air, you will always come back down again. If you drop an object, it will always fall straight down, rather than travel sideways or upwards.

ISAAC NEWTON

Sir Isaac Newton, an English physicist, first noted the existence of gravity when he saw an apple drop from a tree in his mother's garden.

The pull of gravity on an object is exactly the same as the weight of that object. This very heavy bowling ball has more gravity than a feather.

Very heavy bowling ball

Astronauts need special training to learn to live in space, where they experience gravity differently. Before their mission, they ride NASA's 'Vomit Comet', a specially fitted aircraft that simulates the feeling of weightlessness. They also practise underwater in a huge swimming pool called the Neutral Buoyancy Laboratory.

ACTIVITY

This astronaut is floating in zero gravity inside her space station. Spot and circle 10 differences between the two images.

CHECK THE ANSWERS AT THE BACK OF THE BOOK!

MAGICAL MAGNETS

Magnetism is all about electrons — the tiny particles that whizz around the nucleus of an atom. Each electron behaves like a tiny magnet with a north and south pole. When an atom's electrons are all lined up, pointing either north or south, it becomes magnetic.

The Earth itself is a magnet. This is because its core is made of liquid nickel and iron. The Earth rotates, making the liquid swirl around and generate a protective magnetic field around the planet.

The Earth has two north poles and two south poles. The **geographic** north and south poles stay at the points where the Earth's axis passes through the planet's surface. The **magnetic** north and south poles occur wherever the Earth's magnetic field points straight into and out of the Earth at any given time.

A compass aims towards the magnetic North Pole and not the geographic North Pole.

Sometimes the Earth's magnetic field flips, so that it flows from north to south instead of south to north. Scientists don't yet understand why this happens.

ACTIVITY

Look at the panel of objects. Which objects would be attracted to the magnet? Draw each one clinging to it.

Silver spoon

Gold ring

Banana

Tin can

Key

Skipping rope

Aluminium fizzy drink can

Rubber duck

Paper clips

Nails

CHECK THE ANSWERS AT THE BACK OF THE BOOK!

EXAMINING ELEMENTS

Everything in the Universe is made up of elements. An element is a substance that can't be divided further into simpler substances. Our bodies are made up of three main elements. We are 65% oxygen, 18.5% carbon and 9.5% hydrogen.

Elements are organised in a periodic table, which groups them according to how they behave. This helps scientists predict and explain how the elements will react with each other.

ACTIVITY

Unscramble the letters to reveal the elements that are commonly known metals. The pictures will help you!

1. NORI

4. INUMMIALU

2. RISLEV

5. LOGD

3. PERPOC

6. DALE

CHECK THE ANSWERS AT THE BACK OF THE BOOK!

AWESOME ATOMS

Atoms are the basic building blocks of matter. Everything is made up of atoms — you, this book and your pencil or pen. Atoms join together to make molecules.

SAU LAN WU

Sau Lan Wu is a Chinese-American particle physicist. She has dedicated her life to research on protons and neutrons. Her team first observed a teeny particle called the Higgs Bosun, which is thought to give all matter its mass.

ACTIVITY

A carbon atom has six protons, six neutrons and six electrons. In this diagram of a carbon atom, colour the protons blue, the neutrons red and the electrons yellow. Remember, protons and neutrons are clustered in the centre nucleus of the atom and electrons spin around the nucleus.

Atoms are made up of smaller particles called protons and electrons and neutrons. The same number of protons and neutrons cluster in the centre of the atom called the nucleus. Electrons orbit the nucleus.

- ELECTRON
- PROTON
- NEUTRON

STATES OF MATTER

Every material in the world exists in one of three states of matter. It must be either a solid, liquid or gas. Changes in temperature or pressure can change the state of a substance.

HOW DOES THIS HAPPEN?

Atoms are never still. Even those in a solid object with a fixed shape vibrate back and forth. When you heat a solid, the atoms vibrate faster and faster and then move away from each other. They are still connected, but the bonds between them aren't strong enough to give the substance a fixed shape. When this happens the substance turns from solid to liquid.

SOLID

LIQUID

GAS

If you continue to heat the liquid the bonds break and the atoms float away on their own. This happens when the liquid turns to gas.

ACTIVITY

Draw circles to represent how compact the atoms are for substances in these three different states – solid, liquid or gas.

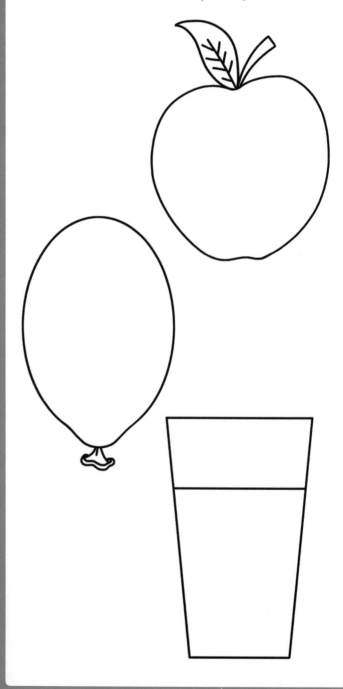

CHECK THE ANSWERS AT THE BACK OF THE BOOK!

Both cooling and heating can change the state of a substance. For example, if you place water in a freezer, it freezes into a solid. But if you leave an ice-cube in warm temperatures, it melts to become a liquid.

GAS

HEATING   COOLING   COOLING

SOLID   HEATING   LIQUID

HEATING

COOLING

ACTIVITY

Find a solid, a liquid and a gas in each picture. Label it with 'S' for solid, 'L' for liquid and 'G' for gas.

1

2

3

CHECK THE ANSWERS AT THE BACK OF THE BOOK!

MARVELLOUS MIXTURES

Many common substances are actually mixtures of other ingredients. A mixture is made from different substances that are not chemically joined and can be easily separated from each other. Sugar dissolved in tea is an example of a mixture.

Some substances, such as oil and water or wax and water, don't mix. A suspension of two liquids that doesn't mix is called an emulsion. Have you ever seen a lava lamp? The lamp heats the wax, which melts and moves around in the water, never mixing with it.

ACTIVITY

Look at the labels, then draw some colourful emulsions inside these lava lamps.

Red water
Yellow wax

Blue water
White wax

Purple water
Red wax

Green water
Blue wax

CHEMICAL REACTIONS

Chemical reactions happen when two or more molecules interact and join together to make a new substance. Many chemical reactions can only start when the ingredients are heated. Some reactions are permanent and some are reversible.

We rely on many chemical reactions in everyday life.

A chemical reaction called **photosynthesis** is used by plants to convert carbon dioxide and water into food (glucose) and oxygen.

Thousands of chemical reactions take place as we digest our food. Saliva and stomach acid create chemical reactions that break down food.

Respiration is the chemical reaction by which our bodies release energy for use in our daily life. It allows us to move, grow and repair cells.

ACTIVITY

Which of these is NOT a chemical reaction?

A — A rusting key

B — A burning log

C — A meowing cat

D — An egg cooking

CHECK THE ANSWERS AT THE BACK OF THE BOOK!

ACIDS AND BASES

Acids are common in nature. Lemon juice contains citric acid, which makes it taste sour and means it stings if we accidentally squirt it in our eyes. A nettle sting is caused by tiny amounts of acid that get transferred to our skin from the leaves.

Any chemical you come across can be acidic or basic. The strength of an acid or base is measured using the pH scale, which involves calculating the number of hydrogen ions in a substance. Strong base substances like bleach have a pH of 13 or 14, because they have few hydrogen ions. Strong acids such as stomach acid have a pH of 1 because they have a lot of hydrogen ions.

ACTIVITY

Draw the missing icons to represent each item on the pH scale.

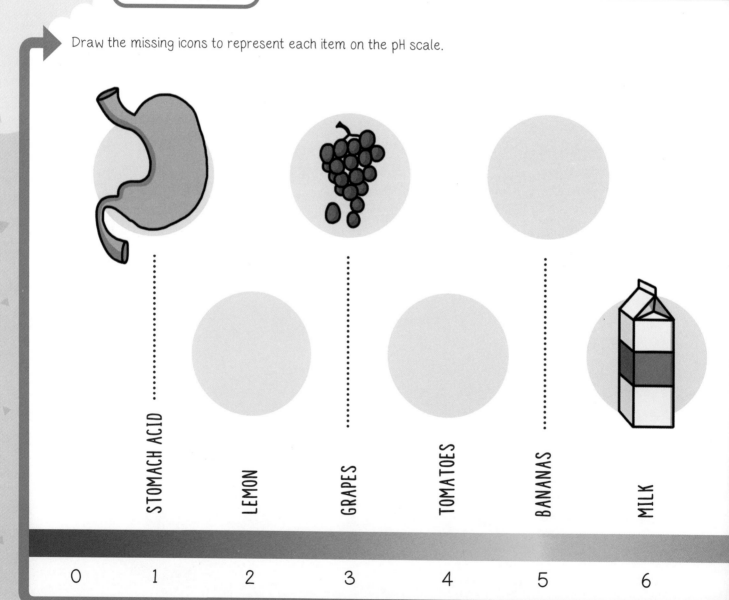

STOMACH ACID · · · · · · ·
LEMON
GRAPES · · · · · · ·
TOMATOES
BANANAS · · · · · · ·
MILK

0   1   2   3   4   5   6

Acids are also common in the body. Our stomach contains a very strong acid to help us digest food. You may also have felt the build up of lactic acid after exercise. It creates a burning sensation in tired muscles.

Chemical reactions involving acids and bases can be useful. Soap is made by an acid-base reaction between fatty acids and a strong base.

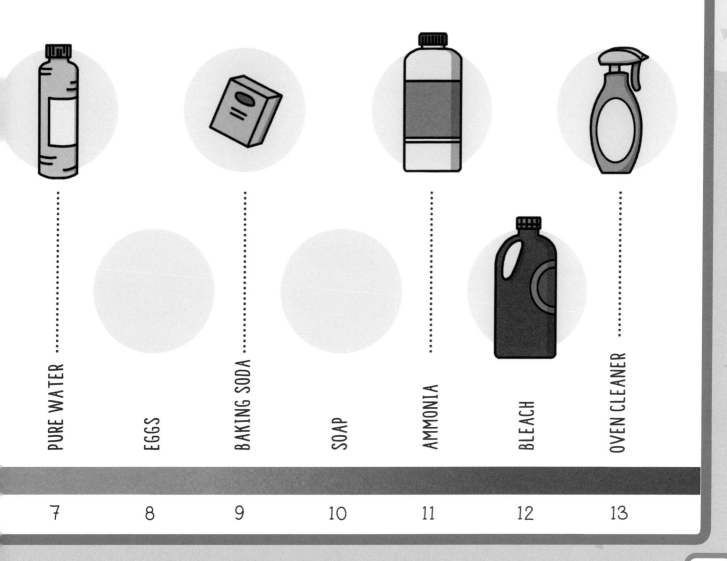

PURE WATER	EGGS	BAKING SODA	SOAP	AMMONIA	BLEACH	OVEN CLEANER
7	8	9	10	11	12	13

PLANT LIFE

Plants are vital to life on Earth. They help regulate the water cycle, form the habitats of many animals, give us food and most importantly produce the oxygen that we breathe.

Plants convert sunlight to energy that they can use to grow, through a process called photosynthesis. As they do this, they take in carbon dioxide and produce oxygen.

SUNLIGHT

OXYGEN

CARBON DIOXIDE

WATER

Plants are cleverer than you might think. Through natural selection, plants have evolved, developing ingenious tricks to make sure their species survive.

❀ Some plants have pods that explode when they're ripe – shooting out the seeds.

❀ Some seeds have hooks to hitchhike on the bodies of birds and bees. Others are in tasty fruit, get eaten and then pass through the animal undamaged to land on fertile ground to grow.

❀ Some seeds have parachutes or wings to catch the wind and fly to new, rich environments.

ACTIVITY

Which of these bees will pollinate the pink flower on the way to the red one? Trace back the trails!

Pollen is a form of plant seed that needs to be transferred from the male flower to the female flower. Bees are great pollinators. They spread pollen that gets caught in their hair as they travel from flower to flower.

CHECK THE ANSWERS AT THE BACK OF THE BOOK!

ANIMAL LIFE

Our planet is teeming with life, but exactly how many species of animal exist? To date around two million have been identified, but researchers believe the actual number, including insects, may lie anywhere between 100 million and two billion.

Some species on Earth are hanging by a thread. When a species is wiped out this is called **extinction**. The Bornean orangutan, the giant tusked bull elephant and the Eastern Lowland gorilla are all critically endangered.

ACTIVITY

The number of wild animals living on Earth is falling every year. Follow the lines to match each of these creatures with their conservation status.

AFRICAN ELEPHANT

GREEN TURTLE

DODO

JAGUAR

BLACK RHINO

EXTINCT

THREATENED

CRITICALLY ENDANGERED

ENDANGERED

VULNERABLE

A major study released by the World Wildlife Fund revealed the number of wild animals living on Earth is set to fall two-thirds by 2020. Human activities such as the destruction of wild habitats, hunting and pollution are all to blame.

CHECK THE ANSWERS AT THE BACK OF THE BOOK!

Humans have learnt to take inspiration from animals and the natural world. Using certain aspects of the way animals look or function for our own purposes is called **biomimicry**.

ACTIVITY

Can you match each example frrom the natural world up to the human invention it inspired?

1 Humpback whale's flipper

2 Shark skin

3 Spider's web silk

4 Iridescent butterfly wings

5 Burrs on a dog's fur

6 Kingfisher's beak

A **E-READER SCREEN**

B **VELCRO**

C **WIND TURBINES**

D **JAPANESE BULLET TRAIN**

E **SWIMMING COSTUME**

F **MEDICAL TAPE**

CHECK THE ANSWERS AT THE BACK OF THE BOOK!

OUR BRILLIANT BODIES

The human body is utterly amazing. This collection of cells and muscles held together by a bony skeleton is made of about seven octillion atoms. An octillion is the same as a billion billion billion!

Your body needs energy to survive. It gets that energy from digesting the food that you chew and swallow. Stomach acids break down the food, passing nutrients to the bloodstream. Blood carries those nutrients, plus oxygen, to the body's cells where they are converted to energy.

BODY FACTS

Your little finger provides half of your hand strength, while your big toes help you balance.

Your nose can smell one trillion different scents.

Your heart beats around one hundred thousand times a day, pumping 5.5 litres of blood per minute.

Your skin's outer layer sheds every two to four weeks.

Your skeleton is very important. It protects internal organs like the heart, lungs and liver. A baby is usually born with 270 bones, but over the years some bones fuse together. An adult skeleton only has 206 bones.

ACTIVITY

Use the colour copy grid to draw your own skeleton.

Can you locate...

THE CRANIUM   **THE RIBS**   **THE PELVIS**   **THE PHALANGES**   **THE FEMUR**

CHECK THE ANSWERS AT THE BACK OF THE BOOK!

CELLS

Cells are the building blocks that make up all living things, including the human body. Humans have over 10 trillion cells in our bodies. Cells provide structure for the body, take nutrients from food and convert them into energy.

Cells are specialized, which means that different cells have different jobs.

• Nerve cells transmit information between parts of the body using electrical and chemical signals.

• White blood cells help defend the body against infectious disease and foreign bodies.

ACTIVITY

Human and plant cells have some similarities and some differences. Look at the cells carefully. Record the qualities that are the same in the SIMILARITIES column in the table below. Record any unique structures under DIFFERENCES. Write an 'A' or a 'P' after each entry in the difference column to show whether it is an ANIMAL or PLANT.

SIMILARITIES		DIFFERENCES	

CHECK THE ANSWERS AT THE BACK OF THE BOOK!

BREATHING AND CIRCULATION

When you breathe, you draw oxygen from the air into your lungs in a process called inspiration. This oxygen is carried through your body in your bloodstream.

ACTIVITY

We can use our pulse to track our heart rate. To locate your pulse, use the two fingers closest to your thumb and place them on the underside of the wrist of your other hand.

Your beating heart pushes so much blood through your body you can feel a little thud in the arteries closest to the skin every time your heart beats. This is your pulse.

Count how many times you feel your pulse in 60 seconds. This is your resting heart rate. Then do the same after exercise. Record your findings. What do you notice?

MY RESTING HEART RATE IS:

MY HEART RATE AFTER 10 JUMPING JACKS:

MY HEART RATE AFTER 20 JUMPING JACKS:

MY HEART RATE AFTER 30 JUMPING JACKS:

These results show that:

GENETICS

Every human's body contains a special code, making them the person that they are.
This code is carried in your genes. You inherit your genes from your parents, which you will in turn pass down to any children you may have.

ACTIVITY

Finish colouring the double helix to show the repeating pattern that is found in DNA. The pattern has been started for you.

Genes are short sections of a complex molecule called DNA (deoxyribonucleic acid). The base pairs of the DNA are nucleotides that always match in the same pattern.

ROSALIND FRANKLIN

This English scientist took X-ray pictures of DNA, which led directly to the discovery of its amazing structure. Sadly Franklin died in 1958 before the structure was discovered.

The DNA molecule looks like a spiral staircase called a double helix. It is made up of two long strands twisted around each other. DNA molecules carry the genetic code which makes you you.

FOOD CHAINS

Food chains and webs show where energy begins and how it is transferred through an ecosystem to animals and humans. Energy is transferred through consumption. Food webs show all the possible paths that energy can take.

The Sun is the source of all natural energy on our planet, so every chain starts with it. The Sun also lies at the centre of all food webs.

Carnivores are meat-eaters, while herbivores live off plants. Humans are omnivores. Omnivores eat both meat and plants, fruit and vegetables. Humans and large wild predators sit at the top of food chains, under them are smaller carnivores, then herbivores.

ACTIVITY

Draw these plants and animals in the correct order to create a food chain that starts with the Sun and ends with the largest energy consumer.

SNAKE	GRASSHOPPER	THE SUN	HAWK	FROG	GRASSES AND PLANTS

1   2   3   4   5   6

CHECK THE ANSWERS AT THE BACK OF THE BOOK!

MEDICINE

In the Middle Ages, people usually only lived until they were around 45. The average human life span has nowadays has reached 71 years. Many amazing scientific discoveries have occurred over the centuries, allowing us to live longer and healthier lives.

Today our health depends on great advances in medicine that are decades old and cutting-edge new discoveries.

PAST MEDICAL ADVANCES

- Penicillin
- Anaesthesia
- Germ theory
- Vaccines

MODERN DISCOVERIES

- Robotic prosthetics
- Robotic surgery
- Organ transplants
- Nuclear medicine

WOMEN IN SCIENCE

Female scientists have been equally influential in the field of medicine. **Marie Curie** was a Polish physicist known for her work on radioactivity, **Jane Cooke Wright** was an oncologist working in the field of chemotherapy. **Alice Ball**, an African-American chemist, developed the only successful treatment for leprosy until antibiotics came along.

There are lots of amazing young women today, too. **Molly Stevens** is a Professor of Biomedical Materials and Regenerative Medicine in London, UK. Her research could help fix failing organs in very young children.

MARIE CURIE

MOLLY STEVENS

Nuclear medicine is a new branch of imaging that uses tiny amounts of radioactive material to diagnose and determine the severity of diseases such as cancer and heart disease. It is painless and doesn't involve surgery.

Medicine involves many specialized fields. Find the icon that illustrates what these medical professionals do.

1
CARDIOLOGIST

2
PAEDIATRICIAN

3
RADIOLOGIST

4
NEUROSURGEON

5
OPHTHALMOLOGIST

6
ORTHOPAEDIST

A

B

C

....

D

E

F

....

CHECK THE ANSWERS AT THE BACK OF THE BOOK!

THE EARTH

The Earth is the shape of a slightly squashed sphere. It spins on its axis — an imaginary line through the centre of the Earth that runs from the North Pole down to the South Pole. The Earth is known as the Goldilocks planet because it has conditions which are 'neither too hot, too cold, but just right' to support life.

The Earth spins around once every 24 hours. As the Earth turns, the area facing the Sun experiences 'day', while the part that's facing away from the Sun experiences 'night'.

The Earth's rotation is gradually slowing, but it's happening so slowly that it could be 140 years before the length of one day will have increased to 25 hours.

The Sun

If you cut the Earth in half, you would see it is made up of four layers. The thin, rocky outer layer is called the crust. Below this is the mantle – the widest section of the Earth. Next comes the outer core, made up of liquid nickel and iron. The centre of the Earth is called the inner core. It is the hottest part of the planet.

ACTIVITY

Label each layer of the Earth shown in this picture.

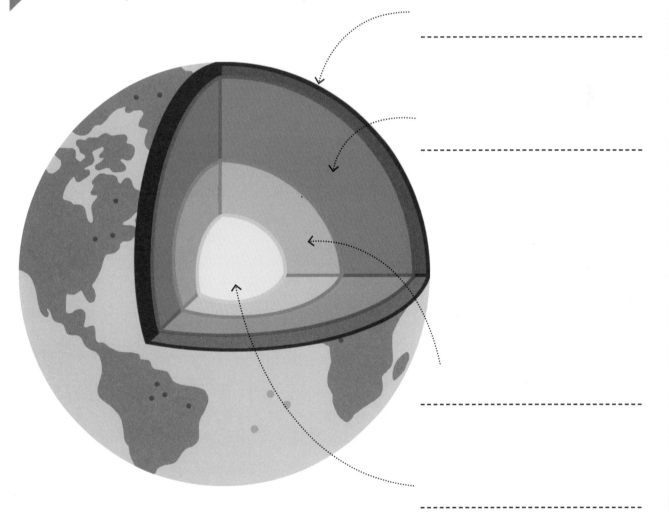

CRUST   MANTLE   INNER CORE   OUTER CORE

CHECK THE ANSWERS AT THE BACK OF THE BOOK!

SHIFTING GROUND

The Earth's crust is like a jigsaw. It is made up of interlocking pieces called tectonic plates. These plates are not fixed. Instead they float on a layer of hot, liquid rock known as magma.

When tectonic plates slide over and under one another, it forces the magma upwards. The magma becomes lava as it bursts out of the Earth's surface in a volcanic eruption.

ACTIVITY

Grab an orange or red pen or pencil and make this volcano erupt. Show the magma shooting up from the magma chamber, along the main vent and out of the volcano's crater. Add the correct words to complete the labelled diagram.

CRATER   LAVA FLOW

MAGMA CHAMBER   SMOKE AND ASH   MAIN VENT

CHECK THE ANSWERS AT THE BACK OF THE BOOK!

ROCKS AND FOSSILS

Studying rocks found on the Earth's surface allows scientists called geologists to answer lots of important questions about our world.

ANNA K BEHRENSMEYER

For almost 30 years, US scientist Anna K Behrensmeyer has been engaged in geological field research in Kenya. She is a world leader in the study of fossil records, and what they can tell us about the past.

HOW OLD IS THE EARTH?

Geologists have found rocks dating back over four million years and can date the Earth to 4.5 million years old.

WAS THERE LIFE ON EARTH BEFORE MAN?

Yes. We know this through the discovery of fossils that were formed when ancient plants and animals died and became trapped inside deposits of sand or mud. Over time, these deposits then turned to rock and left a clear record of ancient life forms.

ACTIVITY

We have a long history of studying fossils and we're still making new discoveries today! Can you locate these four key fossil findings on the world map and write the continent name in the box below?

NORTH AMERICA

SOUTH AMERICA

EUROPE

AFRICA

ASIA

OCEANIA

1. **Velociraptor and Protoceratops in combat**
Discovered: Gobi desert, Mongolia. Date: 1971

2. **Herbivore Muttaburrasaurus**
Discovered: Muttaburra, Queensland, Australia.
Date: 1963

3. **Archeopteryx skeleton**
Discovered: Solnhofen, Germany.
Date: 1860

4. **Gigantic Titanosaur bones**
Discovered: Patagonia, Argentina.
Date: 2014

CHECK THE ANSWERS AT THE BACK OF THE BOOK!

WONDERFUL WATER

Earth is unique in our solar system because of one precious, life-giving substance — water. A massive 71% of the Earth's surface is made up of water. The Earth's oceans help regulate the planet's climate, absorbing heat in the summer and releasing it in the winter.

WE DEPEND ON CLEAN WATER:

1. FOR OUR BODIES TO FUNCTION.

2. TO GROW CROPS AND KEEP LIVESTOCK.

3. TO WASH OUR FOOD AND BODIES.

ACTIVITY

Estimates vary, but the average person uses around 150 litres of water a day. Are you surprised?

Complete the table to work out much water you use in a week.

ACTIVITY	MEASUREMENT	NUMBER OF TIMES	USAGE PER ACTIVITY
Taking a bath	80 litres		
Taking a shower	45 litres		
Brushing my teeth	6 litres		
Washing my hands/face	6 litres		
Drinking water	225 ml per glass		
Using the dishwasher	15 litres		
Flushing the toilet	9 litres		
		TOTAL USAGE	

Multiply the number of litres by the number of times you've done an activity to get the total usage for that activity. Add the **USAGE PER ACTIVITY** figures to get the total water usage.

The Earth has five main oceans – the Atlantic, the Arctic, the Indian, the Pacific and the Southern oceans. Together, these contain the greatest diversity of life on our planet.

THE WATER CYCLE

Most of the world's water is collected in the oceans, but it doesn't stay there. Through a chemical process known as the water cycle, water changes its state of matter and goes from land to sky and back again.

Water on the Earth's surface in oceans, lakes or rivers turns from a liquid to a gas and becomes water vapour. This is known as **evaporation**. The vapour rises and condenses into a mixture of gas, liquid and solid, and forms clouds. This is called **condensation**. When water droplets become too heavy for a cloud to hold them, they fall to the ground as rain. This is called **precipitation**.

A raindrop can take between two and seven minutes to reach the ground.

ACTIVITY

Starting with evaporation, add arrows pointing in the right direction to show each step in the water cycle.

CONDENSATION

EVAPORATION

PRECIPITATION

CHECK THE ANSWERS AT THE BACK OF THE BOOK!

THE FUTURE OF SCIENCE

Exciting new discoveries are happening all over the world, all the time. Right now, scientists are asking themselves fascinating questions. What worlds are left to be explored? Which past discoveries need re-examining? What will we invent next?

These are all questions for the future of science – a future that starts with you!

ACTIVITY

Use this lab page to brainstorm solutions to one of the below:

1 Our Earth's atmosphere is getting hotter due to climate change. How can we change cars to use less gas?

....

....

....

2 It will take years for a rocket to get to Mars. How will the astronauts eat?

....

....

....

3 Earth's fossil fuels will not last forever. How can we get more energy from the Sun?

....

....

....

THE BIG SCIENCE QUIZ

Now it's time to test your science skills! Tick the right answers. Look back though the book if you need to check your facts.

1

STEM stands for...

a) Science, time, engineering and machinery ☐

b) Space, time, elements and machinery ☐

c) Science, technology, engineering and maths ☐

2

Physics is the study of...

a) Living things ☐

b) Energy and forces ☐

c) The study of substances that make up matter ☐

3

The inventor who said 'Eureka!' in his bathtub was...

a) Aristotle ☐   b) Archimedes ☐   c) Anning ☐

4

What percentage of the Earth's surface is made up of water?

a) 71% ☐

b) 53% ☐

c) 45% ☐

5

The shape of the DNA molecule is also known as a...

a) Double helix ☐

b) Orbital ☐

c) Linear ☐

6

The theory explaining the way the Universe was formed is called...

a) The Brown Dwarf ☐

b) The Big Bang ☐

c) The Black Hole ☐

CHECK THE ANSWERS AT THE BACK OF THE BOOK!

7

The adult human skeleton usually has...

a) 106 bones ☐

b) 270 bones ☐

c) 206 bones ☐

8

You would use a prism to...

a) Split white light into a spectrum of coloured light ☐

b) See the edge of the observable Universe ☐

c) Split an atom ☐

9

Electricity can be described as...

a) The flow of tiny particles called electrons ☐

b) The flow of tiny particles called molecules ☐

c) The flow of tiny particles called protons ☐

10

The Earth is made up of...

a) Tectonic plates ☐   b) Magma plates ☐   c) Sedimentary plates ☐

11

Plants change sunlight into energy for growth using...

a) Respiration ☐

b) Photosynthesis ☐

c) Sublimation ☐

12

1	1.008
H	
Hydrogen	

3	6.941
Li	
Lithium	

4	9.012
Be	
Beryllium	

5	10.811
B	
Boron	

6	12.011
C	
Carbon	

The scale used to measure the acidity of a substance is...

a) The pH scale ☐

b) The Fahrenheit scale ☐

c) The periodic scale of elements ☐

CHECK THE ANSWERS AT THE BACK OF THE BOOK!

ANSWERS

Page 8
FIELDS OF SCIENCE
1. G 2. D 3. F 4. B 5. H 6. E 7. C 8. A

Page 9
THE HISTORY OF SCIENCE
Archimedes said 'Eureka!'. It means, 'I have it!'.

Pages 10-11
THINK LIKE A SCIENTIST
B

Page 12
OUR UNIVERSE

BIG
UNIVERSE
GALAXY
STAR
BROWN DWARF
PLANET
ASTEROID
SMALL

Page 12
SPLENDID SPACE

Page 16
MAGNIFICENT MOON

Waxing gibbous
First quarter
Waxing crescent
New Moon
Full Moon
Waning gibbous
Waning crescent
Last quarter

Page 18
LET THERE BE LIGHT
A spectrum of light that happens when sunlight is refracted through raindrops is a RAINBOW.

Pages 20-21
ELECTRICITY
The missing elements in each circuit are:

A. Broken pathway
B. Power source (battery)
C. Switch
D. Load (light bulb)

Page 22
AMAZING X-RAYS

Page 23
SOUND

Pages 24-25
ENERGY
1. Solar 2. Wind 3. Wood 4. Tidal

Page 26
HEAT
The conductors are:
Frying pan / Radiator / Ring / Metal spoon / Iron

Page 27
TEMPERATURE

Chicken
Cow
Human

Page 28-29
FABULOUS FORCES

USEFUL FRICTION
- Striking a match
- Rubbing hands to keep warm
- Sledging
- Car tyres on a road

TOO MUCH FRICTION
- A ring stuck on a finger

NOT ENOUGH FRICTION
- Slipping on the ice

Pages 30-31
GRAVITY

Pages 32-33
MAGICAL MAGNETS
A tin can, paper clips and nails would be attracted to the magnet.

Page 34
EXAMINING ELEMENTS
1. Iron   2. Silver   3. Copper   4. Aluminium
5. Gold   6. Lead

Pages 36-37
STATES OF MATTER

1. Solid – the car
   Liquid – petrol
   Gas – exhaust vapour

2. Solid – the basket
   Liquid – water in the lake
   Gas – helium inside the balloon canopy

3. Gas – air in the beach ball
   Liquid – seawater in the rock pool
   Solid – the deckchair

Page 39
CHEMICAL REACTIONS
C. A meowing cat is not a chemical reaction.

Pages 42-43
PLANT LIFE

Pages 44-45
ANIMAL LIFE
African elephant ············· VULNERABLE
Green turtle ····················· ENDANGERED
Dodo ································ EXTINCT
Jaguar ····························· THREATENED
Black rhino ······················ CRITICALLY ENDANGERED

1. C   2. E   3. F
4. A   5. B   6. D

Pages 46-47
OUR BRILLIANT BODIES

Page 48
CELLS
Plant and human cells both have a cell membrane, cytoplasm, nucleus and mitochondrion. The plant cell has a cell wall, vacuole and chloroplast.

Page 51
FOOD CHAINS
1. Sun   2. Grasses and plants   3. Grasshopper
4. Frog   5. Snake   6. Hawk

Pages 52-53
MEDICINE
1. A   2. F   3. E   4. B   5. C   6. D

Pages 54-55
THE EARTH
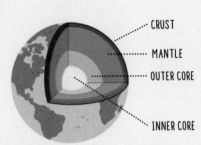

Page 56
SHIFTING GROUND

Page 57
ROCKS AND FOSSILS
1. Asia   2. Oceania   3. Europe   4. South America

Page 59
THE WATER CYCLE

PAGES 61-62
THE BIG SCIENCE QUIZ
1. c   2. b   3. b   4. a   5. a   6. b
7. c   8. a   9. a   10. a   11. b   12. a

LET'S LOOK FOR MINIBEASTS

HOW TO USE THIS BOOK

Stand still. Look up, then look down. Most of the time you are likely to see a minibeast of some sort and the more you look, the more you will see. Use this guide to...

...read about some of the fascinating creatures that live around us and discover what is so amazing about them.

earwig

...take outside with you to see what you can find and identify, then tick off the things you see.

...have fun playing with the stickers on the fold-out grassy play scene at the back.

Looking at minibeasts

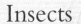

You have two legs, unlike all the creatures in this book.
Some of them don't have any legs and others have
hundreds. All these minibeasts are smaller than you.

Insects
Most minibeasts are
insects. Insects have a
hard outer body, six
legs and up to two
sets of wings.

Spiders
Unlike insects, spiders
have eight legs. They
belong to a group of
animals called arachnids.

Slugs, snails and worms
These creatures have no
legs and a soft body. They
use strong muscles to help
them move around.

Centipedes
and millipedes
Look for these
under garden pots.
They have more
legs than other
types of minibeast.

Amazing minibeast facts

Why do houseflies vomit on their food?
Where are a cricket's ears? Find out the
answers to these questions below.

Ants can carry more than 50 times their own weight.

Crickets have ears on their front legs just below their knees.

Butterflies can't fly if they are cold.

Houseflies vomit on their food.
This turns it into a mush, which they then suck up.

Male grasshoppers sing by rubbing their back legs
against their front wings.

A caterpillar has only six real legs.
The rest are called prolegs and help it to move.

In winter, bees live on the honey they have
stored in their hive during the rest of the year.

An adult mayfly has no real mouth parts because
it eats nothing at all and lives for only a day.

Dragonfly-like insects were among the first animals to fly.

Minibeast-spotters, turn the page!

ladybird larva

Easy-to-spot minibeasts

How many of these minibeasts can you find?
Some of them are very small, so look carefully.

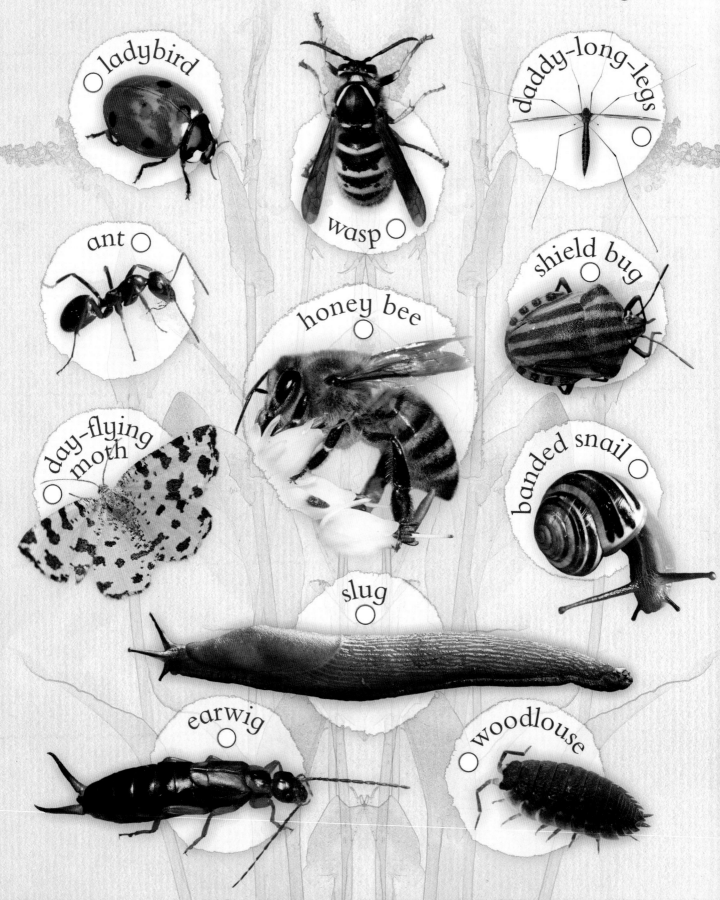

○ ladybird

wasp ○

daddy-long-legs ○

ant ○

shield bug ○

honey bee ○

day-flying moth ○

banded snail ○

slug ○

earwig ○

○ woodlouse

ground beetle ○

hoverfly ○

○ worm

butterfly ○

dragonfly ○

garden snail ○

garden spider ○

longhorn beetle ○

bumblebee ○

house fly ○

house spider ○

Tick them off as you find them.

Harder-to-spot minibeasts

ladybird larva ○

millipede ○

○ fire bug

damselfly ○

mayfly ○

greenbottle fly ○

caterpillar ○

hornet ○

night-flying moth ○

○ froghopper

flesh fly ○

tick ○

grasshopper ○

squash bug ○

hawkmoth ○

bee-fly ○

dragonfly nymph ○

cricket ○

sea slater ○

pond skater ○

scorpion fly ○

devil's coach horse ○

soldier beetle ○

Know your beetles

Did you know that one in every four animals on Earth is a beetle? Unlike other insects, they have hard outer wing cases that protect their flying wings underneath. Have you seen any of these?

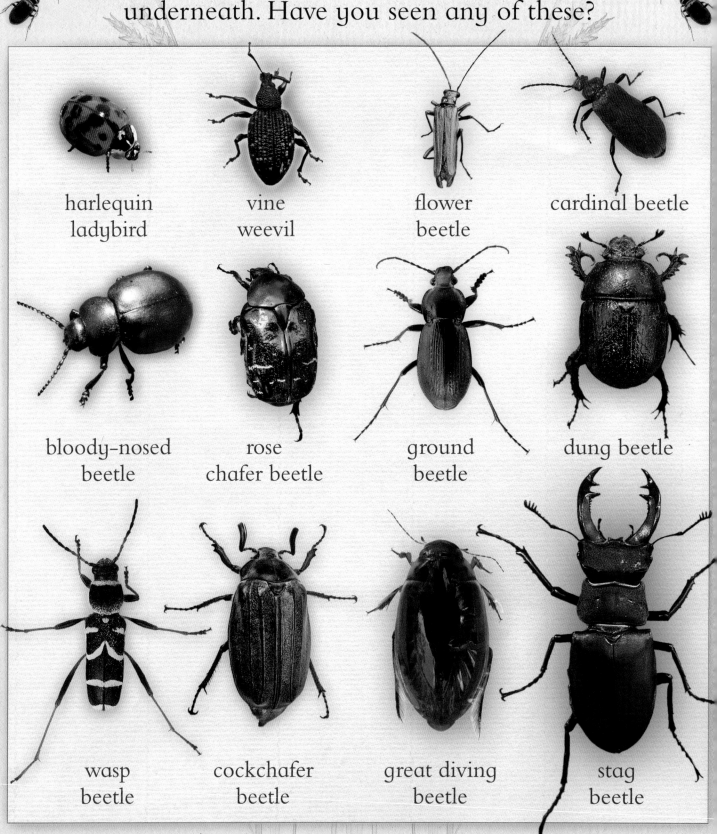

harlequin ladybird	vine weevil	flower beetle	cardinal beetle
bloody-nosed beetle	rose chafer beetle	ground beetle	dung beetle
wasp beetle	cockchafer beetle	great diving beetle	stag beetle